Edition Schott

Antonio Vivaldi

1678 – 1741

T0056032

Concerto

Transcription for Organ by
Transkription für Orgel von
Transcription pour Orgue par
Jean Guillou

D minor / d-Moll / Ré mineur

opus 26/9

Herausgegeben von / Edited by
Paola Talamini

ED 21653
ISMN 979-0-001-19387-0

www.schott-music.com

Mainz · London · Berlin · Madrid · New York · Paris · Prague · Tokyo · Toronto
© 2014 SCHOTT MUSIC GmbH & Co. KG, Mainz · Printed in Germany

Preface

Vivaldi was greatly esteemed by his contemporaries, and many of his works, including *L'Estro Armonico* Op. 3, *La Stravaganza,* Op. 4, *Il Cimento dell'Armonia e dell'Invenzione* Op. 8, *La Cetra* Op. 9 as well as the flute concertos Op. 10, were successfully published by Roger and Le Cene in Amsterdam as well as by Walsh in London.

It is in this context that Jean Guillou's transcription of the Concerto in D minor for Cello, Strings and Harpsichord Op. 26/9 has to be seen. It is included in the Fanna catalogue, numbered F. III n. 24, which contains 26 cello concertos altogether, three of them in D minor. The extant transcriptions of works from that era initially focused on one or more violins. Due to their affinity, however, they can be easily adapted to the organ.

Jean Guillou's transcription is thus not to be understood as a simple tablature, but as a way to use and explore the full expressive potential of the organ, in this case a large, modern instrument with three manuals – and a 32-note pedalboard – rich in specific, characteristic sounds: Within the Vivaldian orchestra, the pedal plays, in fact, the bass line while the left hand rapidly takes over the initial part of the cello solo, including a cadence (in b. 70 of the first movement) of the arranger as well as the harmonic content in the 'tutti' episodes. The right hand, however, undertakes the task of expression and melodic development of the violin parts. In the third movement, attention should be paid to the harmonic accompaniment used by Guillou as a counterpoint in the solo episodes. As before, this is achieved by the left hand, applying 'protagonist registers' and making use of its clearly defined character.

Paola Talamini
Translation Kristin Bredemeier

Vorwort

Antonio Vivaldi genoss hohe Anerkennung unter seinen Zeitgenossen und viele seiner Werke, darunter *L'Estro Armonico* op. 3, *La Stravaganza* op. 4, *Il Cimento dell'Armonia e dell'Invenzione* op. 8, *La Cetra* op. 9 sowie die Flötenkonzerte op. 10 wurden von den Verlegern Roger und Le Cene in Amsterdam sowie Walsh in London veröffentlicht und waren sehr erfolgreich.

In diesem Kontext ist auch Jean Guillous Transkription des Konzertes in d-Moll für Violoncello, Streicher und Cembalo zu sehen. Der Katalog Fanna führt es unter der Nummerierung F. III. N 24; er beinhaltet insgesamt 26 Cellokonzerte, drei davon in d-Moll. Die erhaltenen Transkriptionen von Werken jener Epoche waren ursprünglich meist auf eine oder mehrere Violinen ausgerichtet, sie sind allerdings Dank ihrer Affinität leicht auf die Orgel übertragbar.

Jean Guillous Transkription ist folglich nicht als einfache Übertragung zu verstehen sondern als eine Möglichkeit, das ganze expressive Potential der Orgel auszuschöpfen, in diesem Fall ein großes, modernes Instrument mit drei Manualen – und 32-fachem Pedalwerk – reich an speziellen charakteristischen Klängen: ursprünglich ist die Unterstimme (also bei der Orgel das Pedal) innerhalb Vivaldis Orchester mit der Bassfunktion betraut, während die linke Hand mit rascher Beweglichkeit den ursprünglichen Teil des Cellosolos übernimmt, einschließlich (in T. 70 des ersten Satzes) einer Kadenz des Bearbeiters. Die linke Hand übernimmt aber auch die harmonische Füllung in den „Tutti"-Episoden. Der rechten Hand hingegen kommt die Aufgabe des Ausdrucks und der melodischen Gestaltung der Violinstimmen zu. Im dritten Satz ist die harmonische Begleitung zu beachten, die Guillou als Kontrapunkt in den Solo-Episoden bringt. Dies wird wie zuvor durch das Spiel der linken Hand erreicht, unter Verwendung von „Protagonisten-Registern" und einer klaren, charakteristischen Zeichnung.

Paola Talamini
Übersetzung Kristin Bredemeier

Prefazione

Non v'è dubbio che Antonio Vivaldi e le sue opere godettero di grande considerazione già da parte dei contemporanei: testimonianza inequivocabile ne dà l'ampio successo conseguente alla pubblicazione, presso gli editori Roger e Le Cène di Amsterdam e Walsh di Londra, delle raccolte di concerti *L'Estro Armonico* op. III, *La Stravaganza* op. IV, *Il Cimento dell'Armonia e dell'Invenzione* op. VIII, *La Cetra* op. IX e i Concerti per flauto op. X.

Di numerose composizioni vivaldiane autori quali J. S. Bach e J. G. Walther elaborarono via via brillanti trascrizioni, destinate per lo più al clavicembalo o all'organo. In assoluta sintonia con lo spirito che diede anima a tali versioni strumentali si colloca la trascrizione di Jean Guillou del Concerto in Re minore per violoncello, archi e cembalo, il cui originale appare nel catalogo Fanna con la numerazione F. III n. 24; lo stesso catalogo annovera altri ventisei concerti per violoncello, tre dei quali in Re minore. Va detto che le trascrizioni d'epoca a noi pervenute rielaborano generalmente concerti dedicati in origine ad uno o più violini solisti, opere trasferibili all'organo senza eccessivi problemi, per affinità specifica di tessitura con la zona acuta, destinata di consueto alle parti cantabili.

Le Trascrizione da Guillou va tuttavia intesa non quale semplice intavolatura, bensì come opportunità di utilizzare appieno il potenziale espressivo dell'organo, nel nostro caso un grande strumento moderno a tre manuali – e pedaliera di 32 note – ricco di timbri ben caratterizzati: al Pedale è infatti affidata la resa dei bassi dell'orchestra vivaldiana, mentre nel gioco della mano sinistra si alternano con agilità sia la parte originale del violoncello solista, completata (alla battuta 70 del primo movimento) da una cadenza del trascrittore, sia la parte "di ripieno", realizzata anch'essa *ex novo* da Guillou negli episodi del "Tutti"; alla destra rimane poi il compito d'esprimere il disegno melodico dei violini, sapientemente adeguato all'esecuzione manuale. Da notare infine, nel terzo movimento, la parte melodica di supporto armonico, che Guillou delinea in contrapposizione agli episodi del "Solo", sempre affidati alla mano sinistra e che richiedono con evidenza l'impiego di registri "protagonisti", dal carattere nettamente definito.

Paola Talamini

Concerto

d-Moll / D minor / Ré mineur

I

Antonio Vivaldi
1678–1741
Transkription: Jean Guillou

55 697

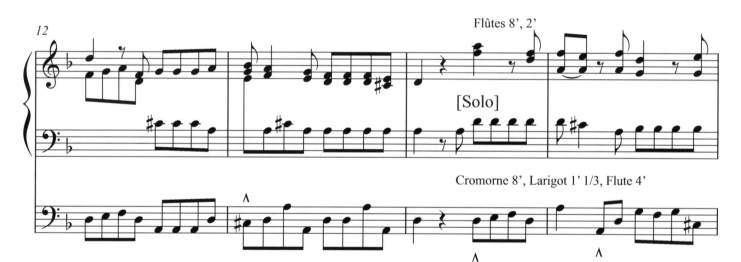

Flûtes 8', 2'

[Solo]

Cromorne 8', Larigot 1' 1/3, Flute 4'

[Solo]

[Tutti]

[Solo]

79

[Tutti]

81

83

85

II

Andante

[Tutti]

Flûte 8', Nazard 2' 2/3, Gemshorn 8'

Flûtes 16', 8', Fagott 16'

[Solo]

Flûtes…

Flûte 8', Gemshorn 8'

… 8', 4', 2' 2/3, 1' 3/5, Trémolo

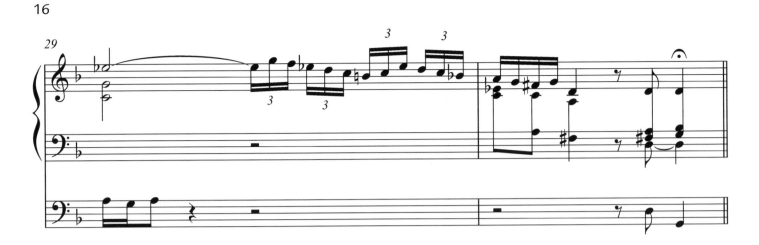

III

Minuet

[Tutti]

Fonds 8', 4', 2', Mutations

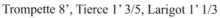

Flûtes 8', 4'

[Solo]

Trompette 8', Tierce 1' 3/5, Larigot 1' 1/3

[Tutti]

+ Flûte 2'

117

[Solo]

+ Petite Cymbale

123

3

129

135

tr

tr

[Tutti]

Schott Music, Mainz 55 697